A GUIDE TO

Wytham
WOODS
the natural place for science

Written by Nigel Fisher and Dr Keith Kirby,
edited by Lucy Kilbey

Wytham Woods
www.wythamwoods.ox.ac.uk

ISBN 978-1-3999-2839-7

Designed and printed by Holywell Press Ltd., Oxford

The paper used to create *A Guide to Wytham Woods* has
directly contributed to The Woodland Trust, enabling
them to plant 6.70 sqm of new native woodland here in
the UK and capture 0.268 tonnes of CO_2

Printed on Carbon Captured paper
Holywell Press
14039900282

CONTENTS

		Introduction	5
		The ffennell legacy	7
		How to use this guidebook	9
01	1.1	Welcome to the Woods	12
02	2.1	A laboratory with leaves	18
	2.2	Bird and bat boxes	21
03	3.1	A variety of woodland	26
04	4.1	The orange-topped posts	32
	4.2	Outreach	35
	4.3	Badgers and other mammals	37
	4.4	The Chalet	41
05	5.1	Veteran trees	44
	5.2	Grassland	47
06	6.1	Woodland Arts	52
	6.2	Woodland Words	57
	6.3	The Woods at war	58
	6.4	Radbrook Common after the war	61
	6.5	Charles Elton and his diaries	64
07	7.1	The Park and Anthill Reserve	68
	7.2	Upper Seeds	69
	7.3	Climate change	70
08	8.1	Marley Fen and wetlands	74
		Wytham's future	77
		Further information	78
		Acknowledgements	78
		List of images	79

01
Bluebells on
Sunday's Hill

INTRODUCTION

Wytham Woods extend over almost 400 hectares (1000 acres) and are often described as the most researched area of woodland in the world, but they are also a place of wonder and delight. They have been owned by the University since 1943, with the first research projects starting up just a few years later, giving them an unrivalled history of scientific data collection.

Approximately a third of the Woods is ancient woodland (which means it has been woodland since at least medieval times), and another third is secondary woodland and has been developed on land used for grazing in the 19th century. Most of the remainder has been planted since the 1940s on former farmland. The Woods are a microcosm of lowland English woodland and this variety makes them both a good site for research and a fantastic place to walk around.

To visit the Woods you require a walking permit, which you can apply for online. There are not many rules to follow – the key ones are that no dogs or bicycles are allowed, and you should keep to the tracks. The permits last for three years, at which point you must make a new application online.

www.wythamwoods.ox.ac.uk/permit

Scan here to apply for a permit

Hazel ffennell

Raymond ffennell

The family name had been Schumacher, but this was changed during the First World War to ffennell, Raymond's mother's maiden name, derived from the Irish O'Fionnghail

THE FFENNELL LEGACY

Wytham Woods came to the University through the generosity of Raymond and Hope ffennell. The family had made their fortune from gold mining in South Africa and bought the estate in 1920. Prior to that the Woods belonged to the Earl of Abingdon, whose ancestors acquired the estate from Abingdon Abbey after the dissolution of the monasteries in c.1535.

Wytham Woods are just one part of the ffennells' contribution to making Oxford a greener place. Raymond ffennell was a key member of the Oxford Preservation Trust, and a loan he made to the City Council safeguarded South Park from development. He campaigned against an Oxford ring road which would have turned Wytham into an Oxford suburb. He also donated land such as Raleigh Park to the Council so it could remain as open space.

The gift of the Woods to the University followed the death of Raymond and Hope ffennell's daughter, Hazel, who is commemorated by a memorial stone near Rough Common. The key criteria of the deed of gift are still followed today: the University should maintain the natural beauty of the Woods; manage them for education and research; and make them available to be enjoyed by the people of Oxford.

Another major legacy is Hill End Outdoor Education Centre. Raymond and Hope ffennell took a huge interest in the educational development of children. We believe their attitudes were strongly based on the Steiner principles where education is not seen as a race to success but a way of developing the whole child, with fresh air, exercise and contact with nature as key aspects of the system. Hill End continues to provide opportunities for open-air education for young people from far and wide.

04

At the entrance to Hill End Outdoor Education Centre

05
Sycamore
leaves in spring

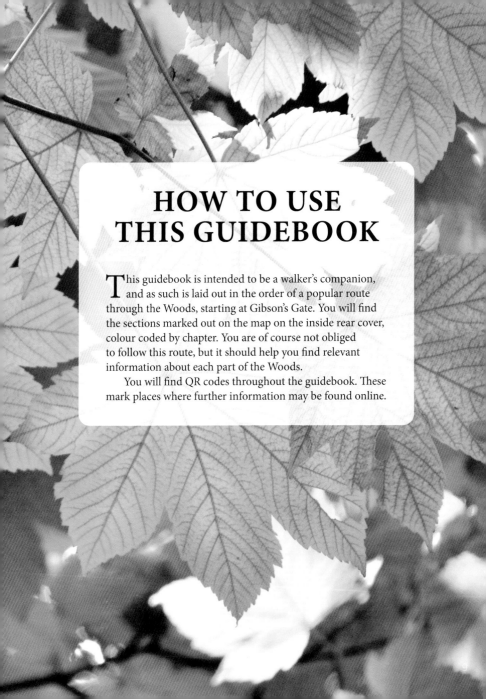

HOW TO USE
THIS GUIDEBOOK

This guidebook is intended to be a walker's companion, and as such is laid out in the order of a popular route through the Woods, starting at Gibson's Gate. You will find the sections marked out on the map on the inside rear cover, colour coded by chapter. You are of course not obliged to follow this route, but it should help you find relevant information about each part of the Woods.

You will find QR codes throughout the guidebook. These mark places where further information may be found online.

06
*A view across
Lower Seeds
towards the
dreaming spires
of Oxford*

01

1.1

WELCOME TO THE WOODS

Most visitors park at Keeper's Hill car park and enter the Woods through Gibson's Gate, named after an ecologist who lived in the Chalet for several years and did much to pull together information on the Woods during the 1980s and 1990s. Although Charlie Gibson trained as a zoologist, he drew up plant lists for the different parts of the Woods and the grassland patches. These showed how the richness of the various areas could often be linked to their history: the more ancient

Left: The hornbeam tree at Gibson's Gate
Above: Gibson's Gate

An old oak tree amongst young growth

the habitat, the greater the incidence of interesting species. To test how quickly species might colonise new areas, Charlie set up the long-running grassland experiment on Upper Seeds in 1986, an area which had formerly been used for growing cereals. Today the results from this study help inform how species-rich grassland elsewhere in the country is managed.

Charlie Gibson had the best overview of the ecology of the whole Woods since Charles Elton, 'the Father of Ecology'. Visitors coming up from the Botley Lodge car park will come across Elton's gate as they progress to the Singing Way. Further information about Elton and his influence at Wytham can be found in section 6.

Through Gibson's gate, a beautiful hornbeam tree used to stand on the right, its characteristic smooth rippled bark attracting a lot of attention. It may have been one of the ornamental trees introduced to the Woods in the 19th century, and unfortunately it blew over in a storm in 2020. The main trunk has been left to quietly moulder away, a process that will probably take a decade or so. The main tree species in the Woods as a whole are oak, ash, sycamore, and beech. As you walk up the road the largest trees are oak, with deeply furrowed bark. Ash and sycamore form most of the smaller, younger generation, the ash with greyish bark, sycamore with darker stems and bark that splits into plates on old trees.

Below: The split bark of a sycamore tree
Right: The bark of an ash tree. Many of our ash trees have unfortunately succumbed to Ash Dieback.

Top: Sycamore leaves
Middle: Oak leaves
Bottom: Ash leaves

15
Ash Dieback
researchers at work

2.1

A LABORATORY
WITH LEAVES

The University manages the Woods for research, education, recreation and
conservation. Since 1943, over 1500 scientific papers have been produced based
on work here. Woodland cycles may operate over decades or even centuries, which
makes them difficult to follow when research grants typically last for only 3-5 years.
However at Wytham each generation of researchers can build on the work of their
predecessors and the Woods are now famous for these long-term studies. Research
on blue and great tits began in 1947, and small mammals in 1948. Other long-term
projects focus on the vegetation (since 1974), badgers (1976), grassland restoration

16

Above left: Researchers locate a grid plot marker using a metal detector
Above right: Checking one of the bird boxes for occupants
Opposite Page: Visitors enjoy a walk in Wytham Woods

(1984), climate change (1992) and bats (2007). At present around 100 scientists have research permits. They come not just from Oxford, but from universities and other organisations from across the country. We are also part of global monitoring schemes relating to forest health and the effects of droughts on ecosystems.

The Woodland Team maintains the balance between managing the Woods for biodiversity and timber production, while managing public access and encouraging engagement through events. For the first 20 years of the University's stewardship forestry teaching dominated, leading to the planting up of Radbrook Common. From the 1960s, ecological research of natural ecosystems came to the fore, exemplified by the work of Charles Elton. Since 2000 there has been more of a mix between recreation, public outreach, conservation and research, but there is still some timber production as a by-product of forest management. At the moment around 60% of the woodland area is left in a state of minimum intervention. The other 40% (mostly the plantations from the 1950s) is managed by removing non-native tree species and encouraging a mixture of different ages of trees.

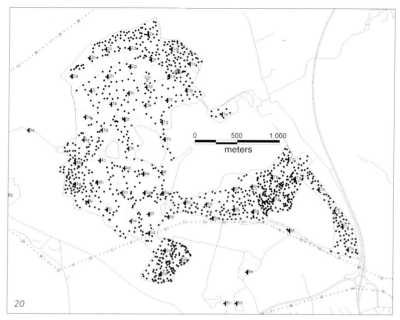

20

2.2

BIRD AND BAT BOXES

Wytham Woods are famous for the great tit and blue tit work that began in 1947, and we now have over 1200 bird boxes. The boxes are made of woodcrete, which stops predators such as woodpeckers from enlarging the entrance hole and killing the chicks. The boxes also often have plastic roofs so that squirrels, stoats and weasels slide off if they jump onto them. Every spring we get around

Above: A map showing the location of bird boxes throughout the Woods. Each box is checked repeatedly throughout the bird breeding season, the eggs monitored and chicks ringed

Opposite page: The flux tower is used to measure forest respiration

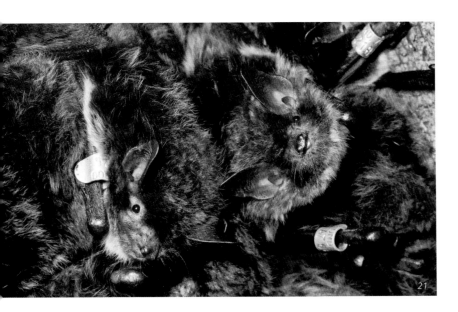

21

700-800 pairs of great tits and blue tits breeding in these boxes.

The boxes are hung just a few metres above the ground, and each has a removable front. This is primarily so that researchers can easily check each one's contents during the breeding season. One of the least pleasant Wytham jobs is the annual removal of old birds' nests from each box in autumn – bird fleas will bite anything if no birds have been visiting the boxes! This is done to reduce the build-up of diseases and parasites.

People often ask why we need bird boxes when we have hundreds of thousands of trees that birds could nest in. Firstly, for safety – researchers and tall ladders do not mix! Secondly, half of the research time would be spent trying to find the nests. Thirdly, we can examine the eggs and chicks quickly and easily, and the final reason is that the boxes can be easily fitted with video cameras or devices for reading the

Above: Bats roosting in a bird box

Opposite page: One of the metal cages used to protect bird tracking equipment

Scan here to visit the Wytham Tit project website

tiny electronic tags (the equivalent of a barcode) that we fit to all of Wytham's great tits and blue tits.

The other part of the bird research you will see on any walk is the metal cages, raised about a metre from the ground. The cages are there simply to stop squirrels chewing on the equipment within. During the winter some of the cages will contain a bird-feeder and a recorder that can read each bird's tag. The researchers can thus study how birds move around the Woods and their social behaviour.

The bat researchers in the Woods see the bird boxes as bat boxes, because once the chicks have fledged bats take over and roost in the roof space. The most bats we have found roosting together in one box is 61! There are also specialist bat boxes which are black, rectangular and appear to have no entrance – bats can squeeze up into

them through a gap at the bottom. There are at least 12 species of bat in Wytham Woods. Each summer data collected from maternity colonies of Natterer's bats, Daubenton's bats, and Brown long-eared bats contribute to understanding their longevity, reproductive history, social bonds, group size, and the spatial distribution of several resident colonies.

DID YOU KNOW?

Because the Wytham Tit Project has been running continuously since 1947, it's probable that we know more about this population of birds than any other in the world. For example, we know that the birds here like to make their nests near their friends.

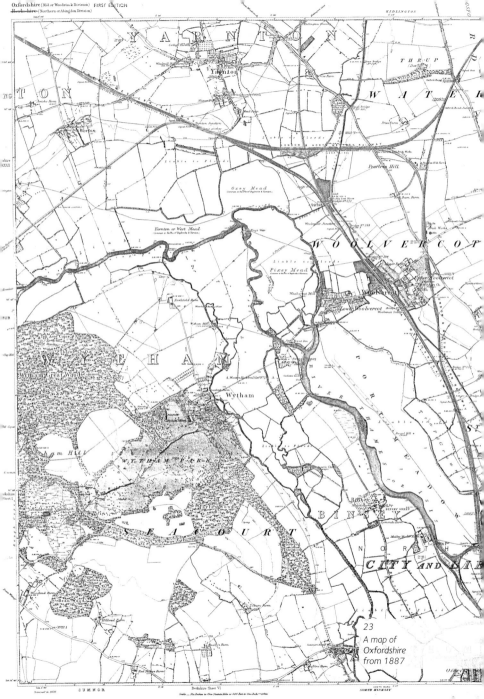

23

A map of
Oxfordshire
from 1887

3.1

A VARIETY OF WOODLAND

Why 'Wytham Woods'? We refer to Wytham Woods in the plural because historically there were several different blocks of woodland that have only joined up in the last couple of hundred years. Rocque's map of 1761 shows the 'Whiteham' Wood clearly separated from Bean Wood and Marley Wood. These are the oldest parts of the Woods – the ancient woodland.

Wytham Woods are old but they are not remnants of the wildwood, the natural forested landscape of prehistoric Britain – Roman pottery has been found beneath

24

Opposite page: Rocque's map of 1761
Above left: Chestnut coppice Above right: The woodbank near Three Pines Ride

tree roots in places, suggesting they may have been open ground 2,000 years ago, but at some stage became woodland again. The Woods would have been a very valuable resource. In 1555 there was a dispute about rights to wood in what is now Cowleaze Copse between George Owen, King's Physician and Lord Williams that had to be settled by the Star Chamber – the highest court under King Henry VIII.

The ancient woodland was managed as coppice where the trees and shrubs are cut at intervals of about 5-25 years, before being harvested again. Each time the stumps regrow as small poles that can be easily made into hurdles, tool handles, or simply carried off for firewood. There is a record of the Nunnery at Godstow having the right to 'fowre burdyns of thornys' a day 'by the syht of her forester'. Small areas of chestnut coppice are maintained in the woods to demonstrate this form of historic management.

The old boundary shown on Roque's map between Whiteham Wood and the more open Whiteham Common, can be traced in the form of an old woodbank, clearly visible as you walk up the road towards the turn-off for Three Pines Ride. The bank was probably made in medieval times to help keep livestock that might be grazing on the Common out of the wooded area where they might damage regrowth from the hazel and other trees and shrubs after they had been cut. It would have had a hedge or fence on top of it and the ditch on the outside would have been deeper

DID YOU KNOW

There are many theories behind the place name 'Wytham', but it is generally understood to be derived from Old English, and means 'village in the bend of a river'.

to make a more effective barrier.

In spring the bluebells growing on the ancient wood side of the bank (to the right if you are walking up the hill) come up and over it but have not spread much into the more recent woodland beyond (to your left). Other plants that tend to be more common in the ancient sections of the Woods include wild garlic, primroses and herb paris. These are sometimes seen as ancient woodland indicators, but in Wytham they have almost all spread to some degree into the newer areas.

Left: Bluebells and wild garlic flower in Wytham Great Wood
Above: Primroses
Below: A 'haloed' oak tree

Whiteham Common had become at least partly wooded by the middle of the 19th century, as an 1887 map shows. Most of the trees, mainly ash and sycamore, are relatively young, but as you walk up the road or along First Turn you will occasionally see much older trees, often with low dead branches. These would have grown up when the Common was much more open – hence the large low branches. They have been swallowed up as the Common turned into a wood. In places the younger trees have been cleared away to give these veterans more space. Lords Common, just before the Chalet, was however shown as open in 1887 and remains so today: in early summer it is rich in grassland flowers.

Woodland development on Whiteham Common in the 19th century seems to have been largely through natural regeneration, but in the southern half of the woods the 5th Earl of Abingdon set about creating new plantations. One of these is Brogden's Belt, the area of beech woodland you come to if you walk up through the fields from the Sawmill car park. Another plantation links Botley Lodge with the ancient Marley Wood and a third area of planting is the avenue of trees along the Singing Way. Judging from the rings in cores taken from these trees, some date from the original plantings about 200 years ago.

Radbrook Common was shown in 1883 as rough with only scattered trees while the area around Pasticks was open farmland: these were not planted up until the early 1950s.

So within the one estate we have patches of medieval woodland, old wooded commons, 19th-century amenity plantings and 20th-century plantations. Each have their own distinctive structure and composition, which we study through a series of vegetation plots scattered across the Woods.

Herb paris

31
An orange-topped
post, helping
researchers find
their plots

4.1

THE ORANGE-TOPPED POSTS

Helping us see how the Woods have changed

As you walk around the Woods you will see some orange-topped posts, often with an upside-down tin-foil tray stuck on top, for example on the left of the main road going up the hill, just before and just after the Chalet. The posts were set out in a 100m grid across the Woods in 1973 by Colyear Dawkins and a team of surveyors, using compass bearings to set up the posts at precise distances (this was before the days of GPS). Knowing where you were in relation to the nearest post made it possible to map the variations in the tree cover, the positions of tracks and open spaces more accurately than before. Researchers could therefore plot their experiments and observations more easily. The tin-foil trays were added later to keep the rain off temperature loggers that were put out in the Woods.

At every other post Colyear Dawkins and David Field marked out 10m x 10m plots. They listed the plants found in these, measured the trees and took soil samples. This gave a very good assessment of what the Woods were like in 1974 based on measurements made at precise and re-discoverable (usually!) locations. We have gone back to these same plots roughly every ten years since and repeated the surveys, so we know how the vegetation of the Woods has been changing and can relate such changes to differences in soil, changes in management, and the rise and fall in deer numbers.

Opposite page: Researchers cannot be deterred by brambles
This page: Pyramidal orchid

What have we discovered? Unsurprisingly, the trees have grown since 1974! Then, a lot of trees were less than 20cm across, whereas typically by 2018 this had increased to 30-40cm. Bigger trees tend to have more leaves, so the Woods have become more shaded. However some areas have opened out, for example where the great storms of 1987 and 1990 blew down patches of birch, where big oak trees have died, or where plantations have been thinned.

Between 1974 and 1991, there was a massive shift in vegetation from a largely bramble-dominated ground flora to a predominance of grasses, particularly the wood false-brome, over large areas. This was driven by the increasing numbers of deer, mainly fallow deer and muntjac. Deer and other large mammals also inadvertently help to spread plants such as pendulous sedge because seeds stick to their coats or get caught in soil on their feet.

It was during Charlie Gibson's time that the Woods were deer-fenced to reduce the damage the deer were doing to the adjacent farmland by coming out of the Woods to eat the crops at night. Within the fence the number of deer was then reduced to allow the woodland plants to thrive and for saplings of trees and shrubs to mature.

The deer population is now much lower than it was and bramble has spread back. This makes life more difficult for researchers who have to move through the Woods off paths but provides cover for small birds and mammals. Bramble flowers are also a great source of nectar for butterflies and other insects, and a wide range of birds and mammals eat the fruit. We are seeing more orchids flowering, whereas before the flowering stalks were quickly bitten back. Look out for common

Left: Fallen elm trees at Five Sisters Right: Brachypodium sylvaticum

spotted orchids and greater butterfly orchids along the grassy tracks and for pyramidal orchids among the grass at the top of the hill.

Soil samples have allowed us to test whether the woods were being affected by acid rain in the 1980s. A re-survey in 1992 showed that there had been some acidification compared to the measurements made in 1974, but this was not too serious for the vegetation. The shift away from coal-fired power stations means that there is now less sulphur dioxide deposition than previously.

There are also signs that nitrogen levels in the soils have increased. This may prove more of a problem in the long run, because it will favour tall, fast-growing plants such as nettles and hedge garlic which may then shade out the smaller woodland flowers. This is one trend we will be exploring

in future recordings of the plots, as well as looking for any evidence that climate change is helping or hindering particular species.

Where the road from the Chalet meets the Singing Way, there used to be a group of tall elms known as the Five Sisters. These and other elms scattered through the woods died back from Dutch Elm Disease. Regrowth still occurs but the trees do not get very big before they are infected again and die. Fortunately, there were not many places where elm was abundant and so the disease's impact on the Woods as a whole was limited. The effect of a new disease, Ash Dieback, will be far more significant because in places ash makes up over half of Wytham Woods' tree canopy. We will use the results from future recordings of the Dawkins plots to track the effects of the disease.

4.2

OUTREACH

For several years Earthwatch was a key partner in the Woods, their activities ranging from setting up Citizen Science projects, to carrying out climate change research and running sustainability workshops with teachers. We also now run our own outreach programme of educational workshops, organised by Dr Kim Polgreen, our Youth Educator in Residence. Kim is currently working on a series of projects linking secondary schools to sustainability issues. She and her students have also trialled elements of the newly created GCSE in Natural History.

One of Earthwatch's goals was to develop ways to enable the public to gather data which was then compared with the work of scientists. The project allowed researchers to understand potential issues concerning public involvement with gathering data, and helped develop simple and repeatable methodologies. One result of the project was an understanding of the different 'errors' that tend to be made by particular age groups, sexes and professions. This information has been useful to us in organising our own Citizen Science projects in recent years, such as bee and butterfly transects – these are walks which you can follow and report back which species you see. ID guides can be borrowed from the office in the Sawmill Yard. You may also

A group of young people identifying insects on a visit to Wytham Woods

have seen our Oxford Plan Bee hotels around Oxford city. These bee hotels were put up to provide habitat for cavity-nesting solitary bees. You can help us monitor their occupancy by taking pictures of the bee tubes and sending them in to us.

We are now part of a global network of plots coordinated by the Smithsonian Institution in the USA, being used to study the effects of climate change on forests. All of the trees within an 18 hectare block running north from just behind the Chalet are tagged and measured. The orange dots denote each tree's 'waist' – a point chosen by researchers to ensure that they are measuring the tree in the same place each time. By measuring the trunk circumference its annual growth can be recorded and in the long term mortality and recruitment rates examined – that is, how many seedlings and saplings appear, and how big these are, versus how many trees die and fall. Thanks to this project we have over a million tree growth measurements taken over a decade, mostly by volunteers. Smaller tree growth plots have been set up on the southern and northern boundaries of the Woods, as well as in some smaller outlying copses. Data from these areas will help us to see whether climate change is affecting the edges of woodland differently from the core plot which is more sheltered from the extremes of the weather.

Scan here to find out about monitoring our bee boxes

Above: An Oxford Plan Bee hotel Below: Orange dots and tree tags enable the recording of accurate data

4.3

BADGERS AND OTHER MAMMALS

If you are walking through the Woods at dusk, you may see a badger running out from the undergrowth. The Woods are basically a badger kingdom, with possibly the highest density of badgers anywhere in Europe. At its peak the population reached around 250 animals in over 20 social groups, each group with multiple setts, most of them in the band of sandy soils that encircle the two hills which the Woods cover.

Even if you do not see a badger you may see their tracks disappearing into the woodland, though some of the paths created by bird researchers on their way to their boxes can look quite similar! The other obvious signs (of badgers, not researchers) are their latrines. You can find some of these on the road verges half-

A badger emerges from among the bluebells.
Badger watching sessions are usually organised in May each year.

40
A badger path
through the wild
garlic in Wytham
Great Wood

way up to the Chalet – try not to step in them.

At present we vaccinate the badgers to stop them catching tuberculosis. We track them using GPS devices and more recently Bluetooth to understand their foraging patterns. Other researchers are studying scent marking, because the world viewed by humans is radically different to the one other species experience. Badgers live in a world of smells. Vision isn't the most important source of information when you forage in darkness and live in underground setts.

Other important research on the mammals of the Woods includes the 'Wytham mouse project' working on wood mice, yellow-necked mice and bank voles. It focuses not only on these tiny animals, but also on even tinier woodland inhabitants: the bacteria which naturally live inside the rodents' guts. As you walk up to the Chalet, on your right you may see rows of tagged bamboo canes. These mark where we track and capture rodents. All are released back to their home territory, after being fitted with a tracking tag. This way we can monitor animals' movements and social interactions without interfering with their daily lives.

Deer populations are also closely monitored. Populations have been estimated in a variety of ways. Dung counts, transect cameras, infra-red cameras and night time surveys with lamps are part of our repertoire. Deer populations have a huge impact on all the woodland fauna and flora. Overgrazing of vegetation not only affects plants but also small mammal populations and even birds, which suffer from potentially valuable nesting habitat like bramble patches being eaten. We currently have three species of deer – fallow, roe and muntjac. You can often find their pellet-like droppings along paths.

Above: A mouse is released back to its home area

PLEASE NOTE

It is still necessary to keep the deer numbers in check, so from time to time we close the Woods to enable culling to take place because there are no natural predators for deer in the UK. Notices are placed at the gates when this happens, and closures are advertised in advance on our website. Please do not enter the Woods when they are closed.

Above: One of the marquees put up in the Woods when the ffennell family first came to Wytham
Below: The Chalet

4.4

THE CHALET

The Chalet is one of the main landmarks within Wytham Woods, its characterful architecture attracting a lot of interest, with many visitors surprised to find such a building in the middle of an Oxfordshire wood.

When the ffennells bought the Wytham Estate the Earls of Abingdon still lived in Wytham Abbey, so the ffennells created lavishly furnished marquees on Rough Common to act as their base during weekend trips from London or for longer summer holidays. Guests for shooting parties were accommodated in the Chalet, whose construction was completed in 1926. The Chalet could sleep up to ten guests, with the servants living in the round huts behind the Chalet. These huts were modelled on South African 'rondavels'.

Since the Woods were gifted to the University the Chalet has been used in a variety of ways. In the 1950s the Warden of the Woods lived downstairs while the Department of Zoology used the middle floor for offices. In the 1970s three families each lived in one of the floors. More recently the Chalet was divided in half, with the front half of the Chalet becoming a three bedroomed house, and the back rooms used by research groups.

Following a recent renovation the Chalet now houses a mix of seminar rooms, laboratory and teaching spaces, and bunkrooms which are available for researchers who need to stay out in the Woods overnight. Meanwhile the round huts have been converted into workshop spaces and are often used by artists (see section 6).

Top image: The Raymond Room, named after Raymond ffennell, is the Chalet's seminar room
Bottom image: The front door to the Chalet

05

5.1

VETERAN TREES

During the last 30 years large old trees – veterans – have been increasingly recognised as important habitats for specialist beetles and flies, fungi, and lichens. They are also distinctive features in their own right. Scattered through the Woods there are over 1000 oaks a metre or more in diameter, which means they are probably over 200 years old. The largest and oldest by some way is the Broad Oak on Radbrook Common which seems to have started its life over 600 years ago as a hedgerow tree before being incorporated into the Woods in the last century.

On the top of the hill the big trees are mainly beech with a few limes. The small-leaved lime was abundant in woodland around Oxford some 3,000-5,000 years ago, but declined and was lost from what are now Wytham Woods for reasons that are unclear. The common limes now present, distinguished by the frilly skirt of small twigs around their base, date from the plantings of the 5th Earl of Abingdon, about 200 years ago.

The large beeches around the Chalet and through to the Singing Way are from the same time. Some are much fatter than others and show cracks down their trunks. We think these show where several trees were bundled together into one planting pit and have since grown together. Such 'bundle plantings' result in a large, wide-spreading tree more quickly than one sapling planted on its own. A visiting German ecologist noted that he had seen similar trees in their parks and that a very similar phrase is used to describe the practice in German.

Beech is generally not as long-lived as oak, and the early 19th-century generation is starting to fall apart. Most winter storms bring a few more large branches, sometimes even whole trees, crashing to the ground. In other cases the main trunk may remain standing but becomes increasingly rotten. Decaying wood, not only that lying on the ground, but also in rot holes and hollows within standing trees, is a great food resource for insects, fungi, and bacteria. Throughout much of the Woods dead wood and dying trees are just left where they are. The exceptions

Opposite page: A 'bundle-planted' beech tree
Below left: Be kind to veteran trees! Below right: A dead beech tree

are where branches or trunks fall across paths – these will be cleared, as will those close to paths and roads that could pose a safety hazard. The amount of dead timber will however steadily increase in the Woods, enriching the decay system. Bats and birds use the crevices and holes created for shelter, roosts and nests, but they have also benefitted from the nest boxes set up throughout the Woods.

This page
Top image: Dead wood should be left in situ
Bottom image: Common lime has a skirt of small twigs around its base

Opposite page
Top image: Marbled white butterfly
Bottom image: Sheep grazing is an integral part of our grassland management

DID YOU KNOW?

Mature trees such as oak or beech can live for several hundred years, but most don't because we cut them to provide timber. Often these old trees have a distinctive stubby trunk, with several branches coming off it. These are pollards, formed when a tree has been repeatedly cut at the same height. The Broad Oak was probably first pollarded in Tudor times, but has not been cut for at least a hundred years.

5.2

GRASSLAND

Wytham Woods also have significant areas of non-wooded area, in particular the species-rich grasslands – Lords Common, the Quarry, Rough Common, Sunday's Hill and the Bowling Alley, The Dell, Upper and Lower Seeds, and the Anthill Reserve. Most of these are the remnants of the former common grazings (see Rocque's map in section 3.1).

52

53

Clockwise from top left: Rock rose, Gatekeeper butterfly, Painted lady butterfly, Bird's foot trefoil
Opposite page: Top: Students on a field course in 1950 count grasshoppers on rabbit-grazed turf
Middle: Carline thistle Bottom: Restored grassland compared to scrub

Livestock grazing largely stopped during the 19th century, but the grasslands were still heavily grazed by rabbits until the mid-1950s. Sheep and rabbit grazing creates short grassland in which a wide variety of small flowers can grow side by side, such as rock rose, thyme, selfheal, lady's bedstraw, gentians and bird's foot trefoil.

When The Wytham Estate was first transferred to the University, it was overrun by rabbits. Then in 1954 myxomatosis reached the Woods and the rabbit population crashed. The grassland started to become taller and denser, and was invaded by thorns, oaks and other trees and shrubs, with some areas effectively becoming new woodland.

Elsewhere the spread of scrub has been kept in check by cutting, and sheep grazing reinstated to try to maintain the rich flora. In summer these areas also have many butterflies that feed on the nectar produced by the wide variety of flowers.

Ecology Field Course, Wytham Woods, 1950. Day 2, 7th Sept. Grasshopper counts by habitats, Rough Common. Rabbit-grazed turf and short grass in front (with E.Williams pouncing); short to medium Brachypodium on slopes; birches and hazels. (Photo copyright R.J. Davies).

61
The Woodcutter's Hut at night

6.1

WOODLAND ARTS

The Woodcutter's Hut, now a base for artists, was built on a site previously used by foresters tending the tree nursery. Some of the now mature beech trees down the slope are the remnants of these seedlings.

Opposite page: Beneath the Surface, at Brogden's Belt

This page: Dead Wood Matters, at the junction towards Sunday's Hill from the Singing Way

The concept of having artists working in the Woods was developed as a way of connecting science with the public. We live in a world where the division between arts and science occurs early in our academic development, but there are many benefits in re-uniting the two strands. This principle lies behind the Anagama kilns run by the Oxford University Kiln Project, where volunteers assist with pottery production. Ceramics produced by well-known potters and amateurs alike have been displayed in many local sites and even at the Embassy of Japan in London.

Work by Robin Wilson and Rosie Fairfax-Cholmeley of The Wytham Studio has been displayed in venues including the Oxford University Museum of Natural History and Harris Manchester College, and they regularly run print-making workshops for visiting schools and other groups.

The artist John Blandy has painted some of our trees for every month of the year including the hornbeam which stood sentinel by the gate, the majestic beech in front of the Chalet, the Broad Oak, and an Ash tree on Rough Common. This artwork was displayed in an exhibition at St John's College and prints are available to purchase on our website, with all profits going towards the conservation of Wytham Woods.

One-off artistic projects at the Woods have included collaborative projects with Modern Art Oxford, Opera Anywhere, and musicians from the Faculty of Music and the Jacqueline du Pré Music Building.

In the last couple of years we have also launched a project titled *Indirect Signs of Presence*, featuring contemporary art installations inspired by research carried out at Wytham Woods.

Scan here to visit our online shop

Below: The kiln being fired

Above: Field mouse linocut print Below: Winter Oak linocut print

6.2

WOODLAND WORDS

May 2019 saw the launch of the Wytham Woods Writing Residency, known as 'Woodland Words'. We were thrilled that Sarah Watkinson, emeritus Professor of Plant Sciences, accepted the post. Sarah ran a series of poetry workshops based on different aspects of scientific research at Wytham and produced a collection of poetry inspired by the Woods. Many of these poems can be found in *The Woods of Hazel*, a poetry anthology published at the end of the residency. Sarah will continue to be involved in guiding each new Writer in Residence, although each is encouraged to take the residency in a new direction.

Scan here for up to date information on Woodland Words

Opposite page: The Broad Oak in pastel

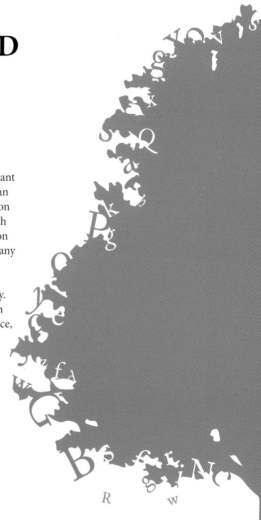

6.3

THE WOODS AT WAR

Radbrook Common, on the far side of the Singing Way, was most affected by felling during the First World War. A series of practice trenches were dug in the south-west corner by soldiers as part of their basic training. These trenches can still be seen today, particularly in winter when the vegetation has died back, although they have gradually filled in and the squared corners have become more rounded. They are clearly visible in a 1918 aerial photograph. Many different regiments trained at Wytham, including the No. 4 Officer Cadet Battalion, to which Raymond ffennell belonged. Also among their number was the celebrated writer C.S. Lewis.

During the Second World War parts of Radbrook Common were ploughed,

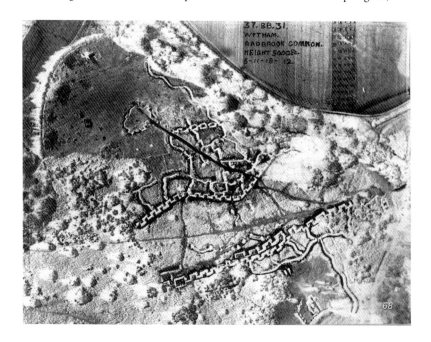

Opposite page: Overhead aerial view of practice trenches on Radbrook Common at Wytham
Above: Soldiers at the Officers' Training School in Wytham Woods, digging trenches
Bottom left: The trenches can still be made out when covered in vegetation
Bottom right: They are one of the most spectacular areas to see bluebells

although they would not have produced much food as the soil is quite poor. Other parts of the Woods were felled for the war effort. Charles Elton's diaries (see section 6.5) give us a first-hand account of the impact:

> *"21 September 1945. There is much sycamore cutting by the Ministry of Supply men in the far part of Common Piece, leaving open wood cleared of all except selected trees, and with underbrush and toppings burned. Tracks rather badly cut up by lorries."*

Aerial photographs from 1946 show much of the north of the woods with only a very open canopy.

However the Woods seem to have recovered fairly quickly, as Elton notes:

> *"10 June 1947 Areas thinned of sycamore a year or two ago by the Ministry of Supply are thickly growing up with coppice of sycamore and elder, and ground vegetation. 23 September 1947 Near Lord's Common a lot of sycamore coppice about 8 ft. high is coming up after the Ministry cuttings two years ago."*

This photograph from the 1950s shows the sort of coppiced sycamore regrowth he was describing.

Left: An aerial photograph of the Woods taken in 1946
Right: Students on a field course in 1950 make their way through an area of coppiced sycamore

6.4

RADBROOK COMMON AFTER THE WAR

When the University first acquired the Woods, it made the Forestry Department responsible for managing them. The department's aim was to improve, maintain and use the woodland in accordance with forestry best practice, in order to teach students of forestry. The Woods were to be worked so as to create an irregular mixed broadleaved high forest, not necessarily of uniform composition throughout, nor precluding the use of coniferous species on short rotations.

Consequently, the Department set about planting Radbrook Common with a mixture of different species. The abbrevations on this map extract show the main crop species and planting date, so the stand at the top left – Be '48-49 – consists of

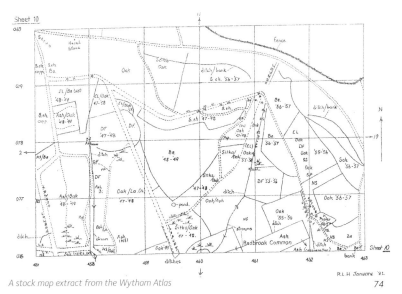

A stock map extract from the Wytham Atlas

74

Radbrook Common being planted in the 1950s

beech planted in the winter of 1948-49. NS refers to Norway spruce, DF Douglas fir, SS to Sitka spruce, and SP to Scots pine.

These are the plantations that you look down on from the Singing Way between The Five Sisters and My Lady's Seat. Similar plantations were created further along the Singing Way on former arable fields, connecting up the main block of woodland with Marley Wood.

After 1961 little management took place and the stands had become rather dark and dense. Thinning over the last decade has removed most of the conifer nurse crops (trees intended to help the primary crop grow straight

and tall before being cut down to give it more space) and opening them out will allow the development of a more varied structure below. Most of the wood harvested, such as the large piles of wood that you can see along the Singing Way, goes for firewood locally.

DID YOU KNOW?

The plantation known as Pasticks is the location of a crime scene in Colin Dexter's Inspector Morse novel, *The Way Through the Woods*.

Above: Logs stacked along the Singing Way Below: Dense trees in one of the Dawkins vegetation plots

6.5

CHARLES ELTON AND HIS DIARIES

Scan here to access
the Elton Archive

Charles Elton was the Director of the Bureau of Animal Population from 1932 to 1965. He is often described as the Father of Ecology and his books such as *The pattern of animal communities* and *The ecology of invasions by animals and plants* are still worth reading. He took a keen interest in the Woods as soon as they passed into the University's possession. His diaries for the period 1942-1965 detail more than 400 visits to the Woods, providing a fascinating view of the area as it was sixty years ago.

Ecology Field Course, Wytham Woods, 1950. Day 6, 11th Sept. Woodland habitat patterns. Woods N.W. of Chalet. Fallen hawthorn trunk on plateau coppice area of Group 1. L. to r.: Miss S. Chapman, R.S.Miller, C.Elton, G. Williams, M.J.Davies. (B.A.P. Strip 7.1.).

Opposite page: Charles Elton is pictured in this photograph from 1950 Above: The plaque commemorating Elton Right: One of Elton's labels still in use

During the 1950s Elton became increasingly concerned about the way the Forestry Department was managing the site. This led to a major debate: were the Woods primarily a 'model teaching forest' for the foresters, demonstrating best forestry practice, or should they be managed primarily as a resource for ecological research? As a result of Elton's advocacy, in 1961 the University decided on the latter, and that policy has continued ever since.

Elton (seated, holding the equipment) was particularly interested in dead wood and its decay, and study of the animals found in rotting logs featured strongly in the autumn field courses he ran in the 1950s. He returned to such studies after retiring in 1965 and arranged for various logs to be left alone so their decay could be followed over the years: at least one such labelled log survives.

A plaque along the Singing Way commemorates Charles Elton's contribution to the Woods. It was placed there in 2015 by his children and grandchildren, who also provided new trees to replace some of the old collapsing beech and hornbeam alongside the track.

81
A view across
Wytham Park

07

7.1

THE PARK AND ANTHILL RESERVE

Scan here to view clips from the BBC oak tree documentary

If you sit on the bench to the left of the Singing Way, you will see Wytham Park stretching out before you. At the far end of the Park you can usually just make out the chimneys of Wytham Abbey.

The Earls of Abingdon created part of the Park by thinning out the woodland into an 'instant' parkland. The Park used to be known for the importance of the invertebrates living in the dead wood of the mature oak trees, but unfortunately due to changes in tenant farmers and subsequent ploughing and application of fertilisers we have lost many of these veterans. In the last decade we have started a replanting schedule, and there are now more than 40 young trees in the Park.

The oak tree filmed for the BBC documentary *Oak Tree: Nature's Greatest Survivor* stands within the Park. This film sees George McGavin investigating the intricacies of the oak, and the fascinating transformations it undergoes over the course of a year.

The Anthill Reserve is the meadow immediately in front of you, set up by Charles Elton in the 1950s. This is

The bench overlooking the park

one our most diverse meadows and is classified as 'ancient'. A grassland can be dated through the size of its anthills, so while our records only go back to the mid-century, we can estimate that this meadow is well over 100 years old. Not only does it contain three soil types (limestone rich, calcareous sands and Oxford clays), but it also features a calcareous flush where spring water emerges from the boundary between the sands and the clays. These springs are an important ecological feature in Wytham and have created Marley Fen. They feed all our ponds, and in the past provided drinking water for Wytham Village.

7.2

UPPER SEEDS

Upper Seeds is a limestone grassland at the very top of Wytham Hill extensively used for research into plant ecology of grassland. They are the fenced-off area on your left as you walk from My Lady's Seat back towards the car park, with another grassland block – the Dell – sloping down to the right.

The triangular area of ploughed land immediately behind the two benches at the top of the hill is where we maintain populations of rare arable weeds. This is done by ploughing the site – half of it in autumn and half in spring. Species such as corn cleavers were once very widespread but the use of herbicides means that they have now disappeared from most cereal crops. Unsprayed but disturbed ground is therefore important for preserving this aspect of our diverse flora.

The rest of Upper Seeds was also arable until the early 1980s, but now it is grazed or mown at different times of the year to help us understand how quickly areas of species rich grassland can be restored once cropping has ceased.

83
The arable
weed plot

7.3

CLIMATE CHANGE

Upper Seeds has also been the site for various climate change studies. In the 1990s 5m x 5m plots had shelters fitted that automatically covered them once a set amount of rain had fallen, and underground heating cables warmed the soils in winter. Currently another project called 'The Raindrop Experiment' is running in a different part of the grassland. Water is collected from shelters across half the plots (so that they suffer more from drought) and added to the other half which are then better able to survive and grow in hot summers. This should allow us to predict more accurately how climate change is likely to affect species-rich grassland.

Since 1992 a meteorological station has been measuring the weather at Wytham. Today other microclimate stations are also located across the Woods. Before this point the recordings were often down to individuals taking responsibility to record their own, or simply using data from the Radcliffe Observatory in Oxford.

84
A meteorological
station

Above: The 'Raindrop' shelters Below: Raking leaf litter

Many projects are showing the influence of climate change even though that was not their original goal. For instance badger populations have been influenced by wetter and milder winters: there is more food available, more females survive and so more cubs are born in February. However, dry springs now seem to mean fewer cubs survive. Similarly, the average date for the start of great tits' breeding season in Wytham is now over two weeks earlier than it was in the 1960s. The tits time their egg laying so that they have chicks in the nest when there are lots of caterpillars around for them to eat. The timing of this caterpillar peak has also shifted earlier over the last 60 years, meaning – for now at least – Wytham's great tits are tracking climate change well.

Other researchers are investigating the release of carbon dioxide from soils. It seems that more carbon dioxide will be released from soils as trees and their roots grow faster, and more leaf litter is deposited on the woodland floor. Because more carbon is stored in a woodland's soil than in its trees, this might lead to an increase in carbon dioxide levels as more leaves decay.

Fern unfurling

08

8.1

MARLEY FEN AND WETLANDS

Opposite page
Top: A peat core sample
Middle: The fen after cutting
Bottom: Great Horsetail

Calcareous fens (peat-forming wetlands fed by mineral-rich springs) are one of the most threatened habitats in the UK. At its deepest point, Marley Fen contains over four metres of peat (vegetation that has only partially decayed) that has been deposited over at least the last 10,000 years and is estimated to store around 450 tonnes of carbon. The whole site is fed by springs emerging where Jurassic Corallian sands meet Oxford Clay, and is home to a diverse ecosystem including some extremely rare invertebrates.

In 2000 a project was set up to restore Marley Fen to its full extent and to try to bring back its plant diversity. The fen had been receiving the wrong levels of nutrients and drying out as its water catchment area had been planted with conifers in the 1950s. Since then the conifers have been felled and the trees encroaching on the fen have been removed. Around 40% of the area dominated by common reed is now cut annually to make the reeds less vigorous and allow other wetland plant species to get established. Future plans may well involve an attempt to restore two fens in the adjacent valleys, which at present are both wet willow woodland.

Wytham Woods also contain a number of spring-fed ponds, the oldest dating from the late 18th century. By 2000 all but one had been invaded by willow scrub. Since then we have carried out a programme of restoration, and in the last few years extra ponds have been created in Radbrook Common.

Many flushes (areas where springs emerge), were planted with trees during the 1950s. You can spot the former wetlands by the amount of sedges that remain.

91
Signs of
Ash Dieback

WYTHAM'S FUTURE

Woods have always changed and always will: the tree species favoured and how they are managed depends on the needs of the local area at the time. Up until the late 19th century oak and hazel were favoured crops, managed as coppice-with-standards; from the middle of the 19th century through to the mid-twentieth century game management was often favoured, and the Woods were augmented by ornamental plantings. After the Second World War, timber production was seen as crucial, while latterly recreation, conservation and sustainability have become the key drivers of management.

The continued tenure of the University and the development of research activities are guaranteed. We are however moving into uncertain times in terms of the UK's climate and the range of pests and diseases arriving here. The Woods will still be dominated by trees,

but what kinds of tree, and how old they are, may change drastically. The effects of more extreme events such as gales and droughts will be key parts of any changes. The changes in the next 40 to 50 years might well be at a pace and scale that we have never seen before, with ash in particular likely to become much less abundant.

However, the many hundreds of scientific papers published from research carried out at Wytham Woods have made an enormous contribution towards a greater understanding of ecology, giving scientists across the world new insights into how these changes will affect us and how we can adapt to them. New research projects will be set up and existing ones continued. The results that come from these will add to Wytham's already impressive contribution to our understanding of how our planet works.

Measuring tree growth, 92

FURTHER INFORMATION

Scan here to access *The Laboratory With Leaves* video series

Up-to-date information about Wytham Woods can be found online at www.wythamwoods.ox.ac.uk, where we list upcoming events, recent news, and provide summaries of most research project groups. You can also follow our social media accounts on Facebook, Twitter, Instagram, and YouTube.

A series of short films titled *The Laboratory With Leaves* can be found on the University's YouTube channel, providing a glimpse behind the scenes of various research projects taking place in Wytham Woods.

Further in-depth information can be found in *Wytham Woods: Oxford's Ecological Laboratory*, edited by Peter Savill, Christopher Perrins, Keith Kirby and Nigel Fisher, and published by Oxford University Press (2011). A new volume about Wytham Woods is also currently in production with OUP.

ACKNOWLEDGEMENTS

The authors and editor would like to thank all those who contributed to the production of this book, namely: Tanesha Allen, Julius Bright-Ross, Ben Burrows, Eleanor Cole, Andrew Hector, Mervyn Hughes, Grace Ironside, Curt Lamberth, Danielle Linton, Thomas Marshall, Keith McMahon, Aura Raulo, Charlene Rowley and Ming-shan Tsai.

Thanks also go to the Woodland Team: Kevin Crawford, Nick Ewart and Neil Havercroft, whose hard work in all weathers is essential for keeping the Woods in good condition. Furthermore, without the support provided to the team by Deborah Steyl the production of this guidebook would not have been possible.

LIST OF IMAGES

Front cover
Blue tit at nest box – Andrew Harrington

Introduction
01. Bluebells on Sunday's Hill – Lucy Kilbey
02. Hazel ffennell – reproduced from the painting by Harold Speed
03. Raymond ffennell – reproduced from the painting by Harold Speed
04. Hill End – Lucy Kilbey
05. Sycamore leaves – Lucy Kilbey

1.1 Welcome to the Woods
06. Oxford View – Lucy Kilbey
07. Hornbeam – Lucy Kilbey
08. Gibson's Gate – Lucy Kilbey
09. Old oak amongst young growth – Keith Kirby
10. Sycamore bark – Keith Kirby
11. Ash bark – Keith Kirby
12. Sycamore leaves – Keith Kirby
13. Oak leaves – Keith Kirby
14. Ash leaves – Keith Kirby

2.1 A laboratory with leaves
15. Ash dieback researchers – Andrew Bailey
16. Visitors to the Woods – Lucy Kilbey
17. Researchers locating a grid plot – Keith Kirby
18. Checking a bird box – Keith Kirby
19. The flux tower – Lucy Kilbey

2.2 Bird and bat boxes
20. Map of bird boxes – The Wytham Tit Project
21. Bats – Andrew Harrington
22. Cage – Lucy Kilbey

3.1 A variety of woodland
23. Ordnance Survey Oxfordshire XXXIII (includes: Gosford and Water Eaton; Marston; Oxford.) 1887 – Reproduced by permission of the National Library of Scotland
24. Whiteham Map by Rocque, J. 1761. A map of Berkshire – Keith Kirby
25. Chestnut coppice – Keith Kirby
26. The woodbank – Keith Kirby
27. Wild garlic and bluebells – Lucy Kilbey
28. Primroses – Keith Kirby
29. Haloed oak – Keith Kirby
30. Herb paris – Lucy Kilbey

4.1 The orange-topped posts
31. Orange post – Lucy Kilbey
32. Measuring the Dawkins plots – Keith Kirby
33. Pyramidal orchid – Lucy Kilbey
34. Fallen elm trees at Five Sisters – Keith Kirby
35. Brachypodium sylvaticum – Keith Kirby

4.2 Outreach
36. Students – Kim Polgreen
37. Bee Hotel – Lucy Kilbey
38. Orange dots – Andrew Bailey

4.3 Badgers and other mammals
39. Badger – Andrew Harrington
40. Badger path – Lucy Kilbey
41. Mouse being released – Tom Zeman

4.4 The Chalet
42. At the Camp on Wytham Hill – from *Hazel, The Happy Journey*, by Hope ffennell
43. The Chalet – Richard Ward Oxford Ltd
44. The Raymond Room – Lucy Kilbey
45. Chalet front door – Lucy Kilbey

5.1 Veteran trees
46. The Broad Oak – Lucy Kilbey
47. Beech – Keith Kirby
48. Tree hugging – Keith Kirby
49. Fallen beech – Keith Kirby

50. Dead wood – Keith Kirby
51. Lime basal shoots – Keith Kirby

5.2 Grassland
52. Marbled white butterfly – Dan Paton
53. Sheep – Lucy Kilbey
54. Quarry rock rose – Keith Kirby
55. Bird's foot trefoil – Lucy Kilbey
56. Gatekeeper butterfly – Keith Kirby
57. Painted lady butterfly – Keith Kirby
58. Ecology Field Course, Wytham Woods 1950, Day 3 – Reproduced by permission of the Oxford University Museum of Natural History
59. Carline thistle – Keith Kirby
60. Lower Seeds – Keith Kirby

6.1 Woodland Arts
61. The Wytham Studio – Paul Hayday
62. *Beneath the Surface,* Art Installation by Hermeet Gill
63. *Dead Wood Matters,* Art Installation by Joe Wilson
64. The Kiln – Robin Wilson
65. Field mouse – Rosie Fairfax-Cholmeley
66. Winter Oak – Rosie Fairfax-Cholmeley
67. The Broad Oak Pastel Artwork – John Blandy

6.3 The Woods at war
68. Overhead aerial view of practice trenches on Radbrook Common at Wytham, 5 November 1918 – Reproduced by permission of the Imperial War Museum
69. Officer's Training School in Wytham Woods – by permission of Ann Krasny, whose grandfather Neville Davies is pictured
70. The trenches as seen today – Keith Kirby
71. The trenches during the bluebell season – Lucy Kilbey
72. Aerial photograph of the Woods, 1946 – Collection held by Wytham Woods
73. Ecology Field Course, Wytham Woods 1950, Day 6 – Reproduced by

permission of the Oxford University Museum of Natural History

6.4 Radbrook Common after the war
74. Stock map extract from the Wytham Atlas produced in 1981 by Richard Hockin
75. Radbrook Common – Kitty Southern
76. Log stack – Lucy Kilbey
77. Dense trees – Keith Kirby

6.5 Charles Elton and his diaries
78. Ecology Field Course, Wytham Woods 1950, Day 6 – Reproduced by permission of the Oxford University Museum of Natural History
79. Elton plaque – Lucy Kilbey
80. Deadwood sign – Keith Kirby

7.1 The Park and Anthill Reserve
81. Oak tree in Wytham Park – Lucy Kilbey
82. The bench overlooking Wytham Park – Lucy Kilbey

7.2 Upper Seeds
83. The arable weed plot – Keith Kirby

7.3 Climate change
84. Meteorological station – Lucy Kilbey
85. The Raindrop Experiment – Lucy Kilbey
86. Leaf litter – Keith Kirby

8.1 Marley Fen and wetlands
87. Fern unfurling – Lucy Kilbey
88. Peat core sample – Angel Sharp Media
89. The fen after cutting – Keith Kirby
90. Great horsetail – Lucy Kilbey

Wytham's future
91. Ash dieback – Lucy Kilbey
92. Researchers – Andrew Bailey

Back cover
Moth – Jack Richardson